THE HUMAN INFANT PROJECT
A JOURNAL OF PARENTAL NOTES & SCIENTIFIC OBSERVATIONS

ABSTRACT

This case study contains notes, observations, developmental milestones and other details recorded during the first 12-36 months of life. Although statistical and external validity are limited due to possible bias and limited sample size, this report does provide strong, clear anecdotal support for the hypothesis that human capacity for love is infinite. Also, there are some *crazy* cute baby pictures.

For small creatures such as we,
the vastness is bearable only
through love. Carl Sagan

arrived on

welcomed by

fig.1 subject appears
to be unusually adorable

PROJECT AUTHOR(S)

Author bio

Interests and areas of specialization

Co-author bio

Interests and areas of specialization

If you wish to make an apple pie from scratch, you must first invent the universe. Carl Sagan

fig.2 Case study author(s)

PRIOR WORKS

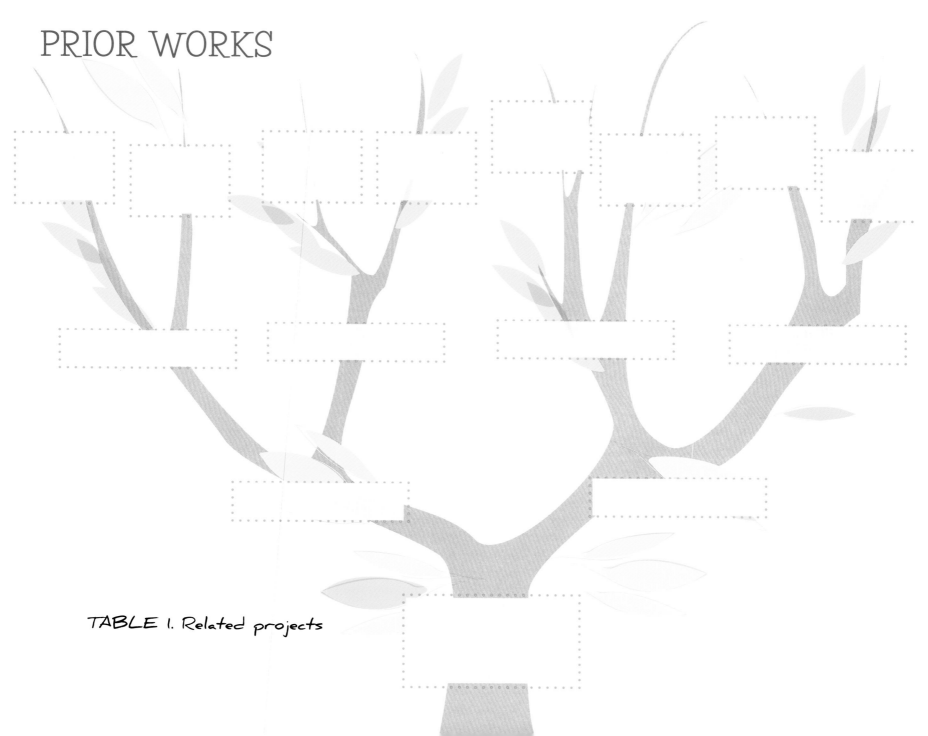

TABLE 1. Related projects

fig.3 photographic record
of earlier related works

I gave a party for time travelers, but I didn't send out the invitations until after the party. I sat there a long time, but no one came.
Stephen Hawking

METHODOLOGY

Families can be formed in many different ways.
This project was able to happen thanks to...

☐ the old-timey way

☐ the miracle of modern medicine

☐ adoption

☐ impulse purchase from surplus catalog

☐ a very interesting story...

"I shall begin at the beginning.
These," he waved his hand,
"are the incubators."
– Director, Central London
Hatchery & Conditioning Center

Many's the day we sat there and
we said, "Wouldn't it be nice
to have a youngster to share our
thoughts and feelings?"
– H.I. McDunnough

"Matthew Cuthbert, I believe that child
has bewitched you! I can see as plain
as plain that you want to keep her." –
Marilla Cuthbert

fig.4 earliest photographic evidence

Prayers answered as today we found a baby as he emerged
from a smoldering crater. Lord is he ever strong! Poss. from
some other world? Martha says that's crazy-talk; either way,
we opted not to contact authorities. Named the fella Clark.
– Johnathon Kent

METHODOLOGY – PREPARATION

Lab-specific preparation

Initial feeling when project was confirmed:

Unusual impulses or cravings:

Developed irrational superstitions:

Felt silly because:

Worried about:

Wondered about:

Was confident that:

General preparation

Purchases:

Projects:

Books:

Web search terms:

fig.5 Anticipation phase

Project timeline

Table 2. Project notes and milestones | dates

HOFSTADTER'S LAW: It always takes longer
than you expect, even when you account for Hofstadter's Law.

NAMING CONSIDERATIONS

PHONOLOGICAL

* easy to pronounce
* doesn't make pun w/last name
* sounds nice w/other family names
* will carry across playground

* unique v. popular
* feminine v. masculine
* modern v. traditional
* highfalutin v. unpretentious

CULTURAL

PERSONAL

* family name
* historical significance
* relates to interests
* no bad associations

Final decision

This name means:

Why it was perfect:

Possible nickname(s):

Other names suggested by crazy people:

This part of the project was:

easy ○○○○○○○○○○○ challenging

fun ○○○○○○○○○○○ agonizing

C. olivacea

certhidea

thraupidae

passeriformes

aves

chordata

animalia

Welcome to Earth, babies. Its hot in the summer and cold in the winter. Its round and wet and crowded. Theres only one rule that I know of: babies, you've got to be kind. - Kurt Vonnegut

fig.6 subject on day one

PROJECT LAUNCH

Date: Time:

Location (precise):   Location (general):

Weight: Length:

Small human's apparent opinion of this sudden turn of events:

Notes and details of the arrival:

| project # | signature | recorded by | date |

EARLY IMPRESSIONS

fig.7 Footprints

fig.8 Handprints

PROJECT LAUNCH CONTEXT – GLOBAL/GENERAL

Local news headlines:

World news:

Popular movies and shows:

Favorite web sites:

Popular online games:

Songs:

Trends:

Economic and political climate:

Those people who think they know everything are a great annoyance to those of us who do.

Isaac Asimov

Top stories in science this week:

Feature story in NATURE:

Breakthroughs this year:

In the next 20 years, scientists hope:

Current debates:

Nobel Prizes awarded for:

Promising fields of research right now:

PROJECT CONTEXT – LOCAL/IMMEDIATE

About early home environment:

fig.9 Home Environment

At home, Day 1

The weather was:

Notable things that happened that day:

The first thing we did:

Early visitors:

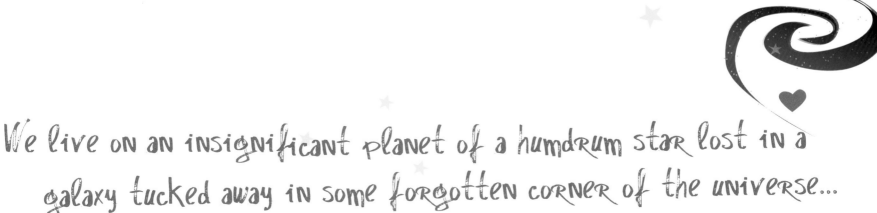

We live on an insignificant planet of a humdrum star lost in a galaxy tucked away in some forgotten corner of the universe...

EARLY DAYS: STATE OF THE LAB

Gifts received during first weeks home:

Primary author's subjective emotional state:

Notable challenges:

Average time between feedings:

Number of diapers changed that first week (est.):

Thank goodness for:

A beautiful moment:

CARETAKER EXHAUSTION REPORT

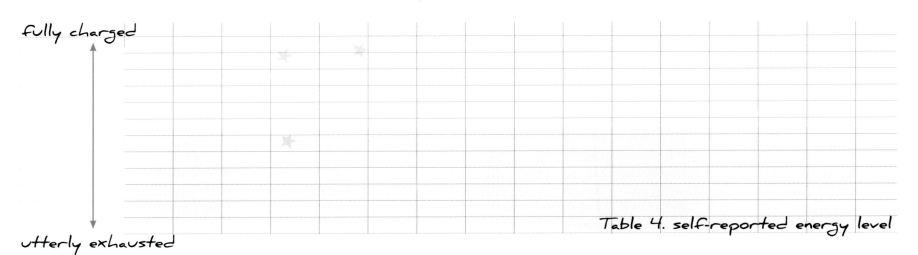

Night #	1	2	3	4	5	6	7	8	9	10	11	12	13	14	15	16
7 pm																
8 pm																
9 pm																
10 pm																
11 pm																
12 pm																
1 am																
2 am																
3 am																
4 am																
5 am																
6 am																
7 am																

Table 3. Hours of sleep per night

fully charged

utterly exhausted

Table 4. self-reported energy level

SUPPORTING DOCUMENTATION

fig.10 Something official

$$\sum_{\heartsuit=1}^{\infty} \frac{1}{\heartsuit}$$

SUM-Bunny loves you!

fig.11 Announcement

RAW DATA

Notes regarding first-time events

Bath:

Outing:

Baby sitter:

Illness:

Doctor's visit:

Pet:

Overnight trip:

Hair cut:

Friend:

December 1839. During first week — yawned, stretched himself just like old person. — Charles Darwin

Smile:

Laugh:

Solid food:

Tooth:

Sleeping through the night:

Words:

When nine weeks & three days old, whilst
lying on his back cooing & kicking very happily.
I happened to sneeze, which made it start,
frown, look frightened & cry rather badly.
— Charles Darwin, notes on his children

EARLY DISCOVERIES

Lights:

Faces:

Specific people:

Trees:

Weather phenomena:

Own hands:

Own feet:

Music:

Animals:

The world is full of magic things, patiently waiting for our senses to grow sharper.
W.B. Yeats

RAW DATA — EARLY PHYSICS EXPERIMENTS

Rolled:

Sat up with help:

Sat up unassisted:

Crawled:

Pulled to a stand:

Took a step:

Experienced the cruel nature of gravity:

Mammalian rooting
and sucking behavior

Moro

Asymmetrical
Tonic Neck reflex

Landau

Finger grasp

Lets play

REFLEX AND MOTOR SKILL
BINGO

Moro reflex (startle)	Mammal-style rooting & sucking	Swats at a toy	Tongue thrust	Object permanence
Seems to recognize cause and effect	Imitates facial expressions	Self awareness	Grabs toys with both hands	Throws an honest to goodness tantrum
Palmar grasp (super cute finger squeeze)	Drinks from a sippy cup	★	Uses gestures to communicate	Pincer grasp
Pointing or poking	Tonic Neck Reflex (Fencing posture)	explores environment	uses a spoon to feed self	Transfer toy from one hand to another
Responds to own name	Follows gaze	Landau/ Superman reflex	Stacks two or more objects	Diver reflex

RAW DATA

Date	Weight	Notes

TABLE 5, 6 Not stressing, just documenting

Brief notes and observations regarding infant's overall mood and status during each month:

RAW DATA: 6+ MONTHS

Favorites

Toys:

Sources of comfort:

Foods:

Time of day:

Things to look at:

Joke:

Sounds:

Manipulation tactic:

Animal:

Programming language:

Equation:

Pop culture reference:

Science fiction series:

Person to attack:

Some NOT favorites

Toys:

Noises:

Recurring event:

Foods:

Time of day:

Programming language:

Pop culture reference:

Medical professional:

Hilarious trick played by adult:

Equipped with five senses,
we explore the universe around us
and call the adventure Science.
-Edwin Powell Hubble

RAW DATA: FIRST MAJOR HOLIDAY

How we celebrated:

Who was there:

Subject response:

According to the song,
Rudolph's nose is shiny, which
means it reflects
rather than emits light.
Useless for navigating fog.
Neil deGrasse Tyson

acute little angle

Fig 12. human young, observed in a celebratory state

CONCLUSIONS

A little letter or two, written with love...

project   signature   recorded by   date

Project after one year

How we celebrated:

Who attended:

What the young human thought of the event:

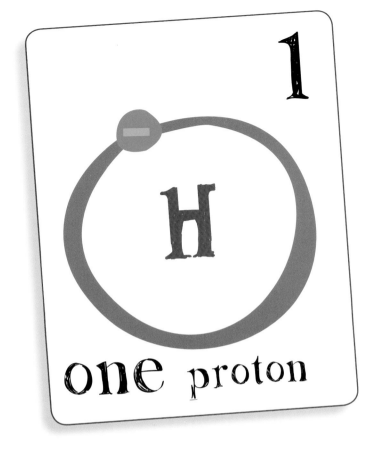

fig.13 observing one Earth year

Year Two-iversary

fig.14 Two Earth years

How we celebrated:

Who attended:

What the young human thought of the event:

Year Three-iversary

fig.15 Three Earth years

ROBOTS OBEY WHAT THE CHILDREN SAY... TMBG

How we celebrated:

Who attended:

What the young human thought of the event:

This page intentionally left blank for use in storing further documentation and photos.

Except obviously for the above statement. And this one.

APGAR

ACT

SAT

TABLE 6 Test scores

GUESS HOW
MUCH I LOVE

NON-EUCLIDEAN GEOMETRY

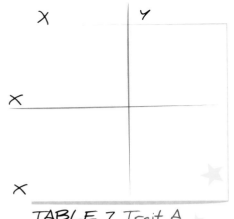

genetic probability of
phenotype traits
(ie hair or eye color)

TABLE 7 Trait A

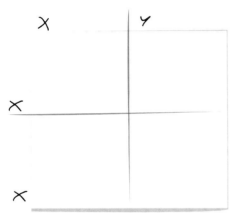

TABLE 8 Trait B

Sample of infant's hair, preserved for:
- Possible DNA sequencing
- Mass spectrometer mineral analysis
- Cloning
- Perspective shift; first haircut
perceived to be extremely recent despite
quantifiable evidence that considerable
time has passed since this sample was
collected.

Was exceedingly amused by his
pinafore being put over his
face & then withdrawn. How
can he find bo-peep amusing?
— Charles Darwin

Research is what
I'm doing when
I don't know
what I'm doing.
Wernher Von Braun

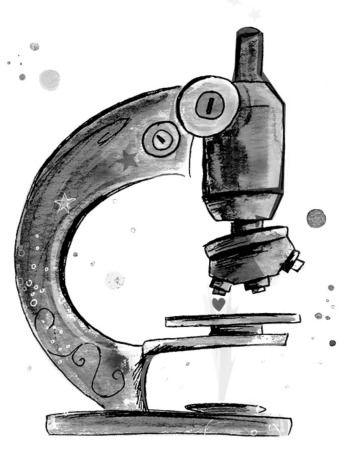

CREATED WITH LOVE
BY TIFFANY ARD & NERDY BABY

Millions of thanks to my Kickstarter backers who funded this printing and to everyone who offered support, advice, and general cheering-on. I appreciate you with all of my dorky little heart.
tiffany@nerdybaby.com

The Human Infant Project: first year notes and observations
ISBN 978-0-9838041-5-4